MISSION: FAMILY

HEIDI INDAHL

GRACEWATCH MEDIA

WINONA, MINNESOTA

MISSION: FAMILY
A Journal to Help Catholic Families Discover
Their Unique Vision, Mission, and Rule of Life

Printed in the United States of America.

Book editing and design by Jerry Windley-Daoust.

Footprint image supplied by Heidi Indahl.
All other images licensed from Adobe Stock.

First Edition: 2020

ISBN 978-1-944008-68-0

GRACEWATCH MEDIA
WINONA, MINNESOTA
GRACEWATCH.ORG

EVERY MEMBER OF THIS FAMILY
IS A VERY IMPORTANT PERSON!

Who are your family's V.I.P.s (Very Important Persons)? Draw a picture of your family, or paste a family photo, in the box below. Have every V.I.P. sign their name underneath your picture.

This journal is all about helping the people on this page work towards a common purpose in an intentional family culture.

INTRODUCTION

Dear Catholic family,

I want you to know that whatever shape or size you may come in, you are beautiful and so very important to the future of our culture, society, and world. Your family is a part of God's plan.

In his apostolic exhortation to families, Pope St. John Paul II said:

> The family finds in the plan of God the Creator and Redeemer not only its identity, what it is, but also its mission, what it can and should do. The role that God calls the family to perform in history derives from what the family is…. Each family finds within itself a summons that cannot be ignored, and that specifies both its dignity and its responsibility: family, become what you are.

> …we must say that the essence and role of the family are in the final analysis specified by love. Hence the family has the mission to guard, reveal and communicate love, and this is a living reflection of and a real sharing in God's love for humanity and the love of Christ the Lord for the Church His bride. (*Familiaris Consortio* #17)

God wants your family to become fully what it was meant to be so that it may share in his mission of love to the world. How special is that?

There are plenty of things we can do to cooperate with God through our family life, bringing grace not only into our own family, but into the lives of others, too.

But we can't do that by leaving our family path to chance—by constantly reacting to circumstances rather than having a plan and a direction. The obvious direction is towards God's path, but what does that mean for us right here and now?

Confident, grace-filled parents discern the answer to that question and make better decisions because they know who they are as a family and what they value. We can say the right prayers, put the right pictures on the wall, but what is it that truly makes your family—and its mission—unique?

Not all Catholic families will be called to the same local mission. You know the saying, "Think global, act local"? Pope St. John Paul II says our global Catholic mission as families is "to guard, reveal and communicate love"—or put another way, to become saints. We can't forget our global (big picture) mission.

On a local level, however, Catholic families are called to all sorts of more specific missions. Just as different saints and religious orders are known for a particular charism, your family has its own charism, too—its own style, gifts, and calling. That's where having a clear family mission is so valuable. It informs our local action of prayer, service, and daily living.

Intentional family living means living on purpose, for a purpose. Committing to intentional family living helps us develop the particular way (local purpose) we fulfill our universal mission of love (global purpose).

Your family has its own charism—its own style, gifts, and calling.

HOW TO USE THIS BOOK

This book contains six missions (one per chapter) to build your family identity, strengthen relationships, and grow in confidence as you reach for the dreams God has placed in the heart of your family. Each mission contains:

- a brief introduction to the topic;
- a few questions for individual reflection or family discussion;
- and a buffet of family activities to create, talk about, pray, and celebrate together.

The activities in this book build upon each other and are meant to be completed sequentially. That said, if you find something that doesn't fit your family's learning style, feel free to skip it. There is intentional redundancy to account for different learning preferences.

Here are a few ways that you might like to work through this journal.

As Parents

You may prefer to work through this book with your spouse before you share it with your children. Especially if your children are young, you may wish to reserve the task of developing a family mission statement to yourselves while doing some of the relationship-building activities with your children. You can always repeat the activities as a family as your children grow older.

As a Family

If at least some of your children are elementary school age or older, they are quite capable of contributing to all the activities in this journal. This journal could serve as the backbone for a series of family meetings, a staycation, or even a self-directed family retreat. Alternatively, the activities may be completed over just a few days, weeks, or months.

As a Faith Community

This book could also be used in a small group study setting. This approach would involve meeting six times, with each meeting covering one of the missions. After opening in prayer, use the short reading introducing each chapter as a way of launching group reflection and discussion, then have the participants complete relevant activities and worksheets during the remainder of the meeting or at home with their families.

Begin subsequent meetings by sharing highs and lows from each participant's experience of the previous week's mission. In this way you will pray and learn together- building not only one intentional family culture, but an entire community of intentional families!

A NOTE ABOUT 'REAL DEAL' FAMILY LIFE

This journal guides you to think about what ideals you'd like to aim for in your family life. But what about when things aren't going so well? What about when we fall short—maybe way short—of our ideals? We settle for "less" out of necessity at times (e.g., bedrest, new baby, moving, job loss, health crisis), but is it really "less"? In accepting the ways we fall short of our daily goals, while still finding a way to keep moving, we teach our children to do the same. Practicing persistence teaches persistence.

Imagine a world full of adults who accept their own shortcomings and the shortcomings of those around them while always still working to do the best they can—adults who understand that falling short the first time doesn't mean you can't still reach for your goals. Wouldn't such a world be a wonderful place to live?

Real-deal family life prepares children for the real-deal world. Scientific breakthroughs don't happen every day; instead there are months and years of failed experiments, of setting goals only to fall short, of making adjustments and changes, continually re-crafting methods, ideas, and hypotheses. Even gifted artists, authors, and musicians do not achieve success the first time they attempt their craft. The same is true of family life!

Given the inevitable realities of family living, is it foolhardy to put an "ideal" into writing?

In spite of all our imperfections, we choose this life. We choose to be open to life in whatever ways that God will gift us with it. In choosing this less-trodden path, we are embracing Catholic ideals and goals—and also the messiness that comes with falling short of those ideals and goals. That means that we will set high standards for ourselves and for our families, but it also means that we will rely heavily on the graces of married and family life (and the blessings of honest friends) to get us through the tough days.

So, are you ready to discover your family's unique identity and mission? May the Holy Spirit guide and inspire you in the journey ahead.

Heidi

In accepting the ways we fall short of our daily goals, while still finding a way to keep moving, we teach our children to do the same. Practicing persistence teaches persistence.

DEFINING OUR FAMILY IDENTITY: WHO ARE WE?

When you think of the ideal family, what leaps to mind? Through the generations, popular media have given us a slew of iconic families. The Ingalls and the Cleavers, for instance, are two families that almost everyone is familiar with, even if they have never read *Little House on the Prairie* or watched *Leave it To Beaver*.

Even within Catholic circles, we sometimes find expectations about the "perfect Catholic family."

How we feel about these ideal families affects how we feel about our own family. Women seem to be particularly in tune with the characteristics of one fictional character or another, judging themselves in the eyes of their favorite book or television mother.

As if that weren't enough to complicate the task of clarifying our family identity, the past few generations have seen dramatic shifts in expectations about the roles that men and women play in the family. Even basic definitions of what a family is have come into question.

Have you ever worried how your family measures up against these ideals? Be reassured, your family's fundamental identity is grounded in God's plan. And each member of your family possesses unique gifts and talents that, when combined, contribute to the particular identity of your entire family.

Any worthy mission can only be launched from the beginning—where you are right now. The following activities are aimed at helping you discover and celebrate that spot.

DISCUSSION

1. What is your favorite pop-culture family, and why? Is there something about them that you wish you had in your own family life?

....

....

....

....

....

2. It can be challenging to uphold Catholic traditions and values when our friends and neighbors have different ideas about family life than we do. Sometimes others judge us negatively for our choice to live according to the ideals of our faith. What sorts of struggles do you think Catholic families face in today's culture? What strategies are most helpful for coping with these struggles?

....

....

....

....

....

....

....

....

....

....

ACTIVITIES FOR DEFINING YOUR FAMILY'S IDENTITY

Your Family Is Worth Celebrating

Very Important People should be celebrated regularly. Use the chart on page 13 to identify very important days for Very Important People. Keep it in a safe place for future reference. Better yet, supersize it into a family special days poster!

Here's another way to celebrate your family identity: Create a work of art together that expresses your family identity. A few suggestions include making handprints or footprints, using magazine cutouts to create word art, or decorating a frame for your most recent family photo. You'll find many more family art ideas on Pinterest.

Talk Together: Our Favorite Things

Spending time together is one of the simplest ways to build family relationships. Dinnertime discussions can be especially meaningful.

Here's a simple discussion starter called "My Favorite Things." Photocopy the note cards on the opposite page and cut them out (or write the words on your own note cards). Place the cards in the center of your dinner table. Take turns choosing a topic (at random) from the cards, allowing each person to share his or her "favorite" for the selected category.

Your Family Has Priorities

There are many ways that families express their Christian identity. Just as we all have individual strengths and charisms, so it is with our families. Some families are very active in pro-life work; others may feel called to work with the homeless; others may be very involved in parish ministry; and still others may be called to a quieter, prayerful family life. All of these are important activities, deserving of our support, but it is also legitimate for each family to have its own "favorite" area of deeper focus.

Use the questions on page 12 to list explore your family's passions and priorities.

BOARD GAME	SPORT	VACATION
MEAL	MOVIE	PODCAST OR YOUTUBE CHANNEL
TRADITION	HYMN	HOLIDAY
MUSIC GENRE	PRAYER	PIZZA TOPPINGS
SEASON	COLOR	PLACE
ARTIST	SAINT	ANIMAL

As a family, make a list of things that are important to you. Where does your family really thrive?

....

....

....

....

....

....

....

....

....

When you have finished listing your priorities, pray over that list and discuss it as a family. Ask the Holy Spirit to show you how to use each passion for the sanctification of your family. Where can you grow in these priorities? How can you connect these passions to your Catholic faith?

....

....

....

....

....

....

....

Our Family's Very Important People

NAME	BIRTHDAY	BAPTISM DAY	PATRON SAINT DAY

Our "Family Birthday" (Mom and Dad's Wedding Anniversary):

DISCOVERING OUR FAMILY VISION: WHAT ARE OUR DREAMS?

At the beginning of each year school year, my husband and I make time to sit down and brainstorm individual dreams for all our children. Maybe we would like to work on potty training with our toddler or build leadership skills with our tween. Each year we have a goal theme that helps us make decisions about activities and focuses our homeschool curriculum selections for each child. We include any preparation to receive the sacraments (First Communion, Confirmation) in our discussion.

Toward the end of our conversation, we naturally drift into what our goals as a family might be. Some of our goals are faith-based (such as our service and giving commitments) and others are not. Some are primarily jobs for my husband and me, and others involve our children as well.

Potty training, leadership skills, and charitable giving might all represent our wishes for a year, but they aren't useful goals. Goals are your "wish roadmap." Various people who are more clever than I am have created the acronym SMART to help us write useable goals. SMART goals are:

- Specific
- Motivating
- Achievable
- Relevant
- Timed

Take charitable giving, for example. It would be easy to say, "We want to increase our giving." But it would be more *specific* to say, "We want to increase our giving to 10 percent of our gross income." We could make the goal more *motivating* by stating why we wanted to give or who we wanted to benefit from our giving. Those statements would also make the goal more *relevant*. *Achievability* is something that must be determined individually. Maybe jumping from 0 percent to 10 percent giving in one year is too much and making a smaller move would be more achievable based on our family circumstances.

The last component of a SMART goal is to set a *timeline*. In this example, our final goal might read something like this: "In order to support the mission of our parish community, we want to increase our charitable giving by $20 each month in order to reach 10 percent of our gross income by January of next year."

If your goal involves several steps, see whether there are any small steps you can take on a daily basis to make progress towards your goal. For example, if you set a family goal of increasing works of service, then a small step toward that goal would be to schedule your next activity.

DISCUSSION

1. What are some of the wishes you have for your family? Think about simple, fun wishes, practical wishes, serious wishes. Don't be afraid to dream big!

....

....

....

....

....

....

....

....

....

2. Many people set New Year's resolutions each year. Thinking back, what is the most successful resolution you have ever set? Why do you think you were successful that year?

....

....

....

....

....

ACTIVITIES FOR FINDING A FAMILY VISION

Your Dreams Are Your Vision

What are some of your wishes for your children this year? What about for your family? Make a "Family Vision Board" by looking through magazines, printing pictures from the internet, and even creating your own artwork. Choose places you want to visit, people you want to serve, activities you want to try, inspiring quotes. Anything that makes your heart smile!

Our family has a vision board for our homesteading ideas. Animals we'd like to raise, structures we think are interesting…things like that. These are our wishes. They probably won't all happen, but they help us focus on our goals as a family. Then, when we are looking to start a new project, our vision board is a place to start for ideas.

Your Vision Can Become Reality

When you are ready to take those wishes and turn them into goals, use the "Turning Wishes Into SMART Goals" worksheet to help walk you through the SMART goals process. Then fill out the implementation plan with milestones to help track your progress.

In your plan, be sure to include a celebration of the successful completion of your goal. Fair warning: Children are very talented at keeping adults accountable towards family goals!

TURNING WISHES INTO SMART GOALS

Our wish:

How our wish is SPECIFIC:

How our wish is MOTIVATING:

How our wish is ACHIEVABLE:

How our wish is RELEVANT:

How our wish is TIMED:

Our SMART goal:

OUR GOAL IMPLEMENTATION PLAN

> **Our SMART goal:**

Markers and milestones toward achieving our goal (check off as completed):

- [ ] ....
- [ ] ....
- [ ] ....
- [ ] ....
- [ ] ....
- [ ] ....
- [ ] ....
- [ ] ....

Achieving this goal will help our family to:

....

....

When we achieve this goal, we will celebrate by:

....

....

OUR FAMILY MISSION STATEMENT: WHAT ARE WE CALLED TO DO?

If family identity (Mission 1) defines what your family is about, mission statements define what your family is called to do. As Catholic families, we share a common goal: we are destined to be reunited with God and one another in a perfect communion of love in heaven. We share a common role model in the Holy Family.

We are dealing with quite a different world than the Holy Family did, however, and quite a different set of challenges and decisions. How do we navigate our complex twenty-first century world to achieve both our "big" goal (heaven) and our more specific family goals (Mission 2)? With a family mission statement, of course!

Your family will benefit most from a mission statement that tells everyone (family members and outsiders) what your family stands for and what your family does. A solid mission statement provides a framework for the identity and goals you worked on in the previous two chapters.

Mission statements look to the long term. Our goals tell us what we want to do in a defined period of time, but a mission statement identifies a family's purpose and tells us what we look like on the way there.

Writing your mission statement needs to be a family affair. You want every person in your family to take ownership of the mission, and people are more likely to take ownership of something they have contributed to.

Just how much your children are involved in this process will depend on their ages, but even the youngest can contribute on some level. When we first wrote our family mission statement, our children were still fairly young, and we did most of the actual writing ourselves. But even if your kids aren't reading and writing yet, they can help by brainstorming ideas, proposing wording, or voting between several final versions.

There is no right or wrong way to format a mission statement. In general, however, a good mission statement will clearly identify 1) the purpose of your family, and 2) what an outsider should be able to observe that shows you are meeting your stated purpose.

DISCUSSION

1. What words describe what others should be able to observe about your family on your very best days? What types of things are you doing? How are you speaking to one another?

....

....

....

....

....

....

....

....

....

....

....

....

....

....

....

....

....

2. Despite our best efforts, reality doesn't always line up with our ideal. What are the warning signs that your family isn't moving in the desired direction? What types of activities does your family enjoy doing together that might help you get back on track?

....

....

....

....

....

....

....

....

....

....

....

....

....

ACTIVITIES FOR DEVELOPING YOUR FAMILY MISSION STATEMENT

Your Identity & Goals Become Your Mission

Take the first discussion question further by brainstorming characteristics that your family aspires toward. What words describe what you would hope for your family to look like? You can even look back at the previous activities in this journal and choose some key words and concepts. Make a list of these words and ideas, incorporate the names of your family members, and upload them to wordclouds.com or wordle.net to make a decorative word cloud to print out and display.

....

....

....

....

....

....

Your Family Is Called To Mission

Creating a mission statement is hard work, and it might not be very enjoyable for younger children. When you have finished creating your family mission statement, be sure to celebrate! Print it out using a beautiful design and have a "signing" event with a special party and pictures. Then display it prominently in your home.

Example Family Mission Statement

Here's the mission statement our own family developed, with a short explanation for each section. If you like, you can use it as a guide as you work on your own mission statement (keeping in mind that your family will have different values, dreams, and goals!).

OUR MISSION STATEMENT

All families do things differently. We like to emphasize this in a way that makes it easy to say, "We do it this way because we are a part of this family; other families do things other ways."

1

In this family:

we honor God through

faith and service;

2

The first and most important thing in all our activities is that we are bringing honor to God. That includes our daily activities, school, work, relationships, intentional acts of faith (prayer, Mass, devotions, etc.), and service.

Before we act, we ask: Is this action going to bring honor to God? If the answer is no, then we need to rethink our choices. Do we always achieve this goal? No. But having this in our mission statement gives us concrete, familiar language to use when we have to talk about choices that didn't bring honor to God.

3

we think before we act;

we work together;

4

"No one is finished until everyone is finished." If you finish your bedtime chore, schoolwork, or other task and someone else isn't quite done yet, then, as a member of this family, it is your responsibility to help the other person out. This way everyone is finished with work more quickly and we can enjoy playtime together.

and we show respect

for others and ourselves.

5

If we succeed in the first sections of our mission statement, then this one might seem a bit redundant. In some ways, it is. On the other hand, a little extra reminder doesn't hurt. We live in a diverse world and a lot of the choices that our family makes are not the same choices that other people make. Respecting ourselves by respecting our bodies and caring for our own physical, mental, and spiritual health is a way to bring honor to God!

Your Mission Requires Accountability

Develop a family mission statement implementation plan by selecting two ways that your family will use your mission statement. Include what roles your children will have in the implementation plan (creation, display, memorization, etc.). You may also want to include a plan for when you will revisit the mission statement to make sure that it is continuing to reflect your family's identity.

Our Family Mission Implementation Plan

We will use our mission statement to...

1
....
....
....
....

2
....
....
....
....

In order to make sure our mission statement is guiding us along the proper path, we will revisit our mission statement on the following date to evaluate how it is working for our family:

....

MISSION 4

OUR RULE OF LIFE: HOW WILL WE LIVE TOGETHER DAY BY DAY?

One of the most straightforward ways to use a family mission statement is for making decisions about daily living. We want to be sure that our time is spent in a way that builds our family's mission. We can't create more hours in the day, but we can create more intentionality in our hours.

The idea of intentionally using time in a routine or outlined way is not new to Christian ways of life. In fact, monastic life for centuries has been built around "rules" of living. These rules give a structure for the daily life and activities of religious community members. There are intentional times for productive work, prayer, community living, and more. These rules can vary significantly based on the order, but all communities have a rule. The way you work together as a family (your rule) will help or harm your family as you strive to live as a community.

Your mission statement (Mission 3) can provide a guide for how your family spends its time and what your routines of daily life look like. Of course, you will need to account for the seasons of family life. That new baby isn't going to come out knowing the rules, and toddlers and young preschoolers are notorious for stretching the rules even when they know better. Teens usually have different privileges and responsibilities that need to be accounted for. We have to remember to leave plenty of room for grace here!

In reading the lives of saints who were raised Catholic, we often hear about the things that the child's family always did. They always went to Mass on certain days (or every day). They always sang a certain hymn or said a certain prayer after dinner each night. Creating your own family rule is discovering these key activities for your family based on your mission, goals, and identity.

A rule of life is about a lot more than just cleaning and chores—it is also about your family's activities in the community, your life of prayer and worship, maintaining relationships, and more. *A Mother's Rule of Life* by Holly Pierlot (2004, Sophia Institute Press) makes many connections between monastic rules of living and the structure of family life. Pierlot proposes five priorities of married life that can help order our family's days: prayer, person, partner, provider, periphery.

Using a rule of family living helps us balance our physical, spiritual, and emotional needs in the daily routine of our family. Looking for the purpose in each and every one of our activities of daily living helped us better orient our family towards our Christ-centered mission.

DISCUSSION

1. What are the things our family does regularly—our daily living rules and our bigger traditions? How do those activities help or hinder our us on our journey to be saints?

....

....

....

....

....

....

....

....

....

....

....

2. Give your family daily life a check up. Is one person doing more than their share of the less-pleasant tasks (toilet cleaning!)? How can we work together in a way that builds up community?

ACTIVITIES FOR A FAMILY RULE OF LIFE

Your Family Needs Role Models

As Catholics we have a wealth of saintly examples to help us live our family life to its fullest. While living our own mission, we can learn from others who have navigated Catholic family and relationships. Do a little research to learn about one of these families and then create a holy card for the family you chose, adding the prayer that you compose in the next activity. Consider making it digital so you can print off a copy for every member of your family.

Don't forget to add your new family patron's feast date to your chart from Mission 1!

Who are the people in the family?

....

....

....

....

....

Holiness Runs In the Family

These saints all come from the same family. Read their stories online for inspiration. Maybe you'll even choose one as your family's patron saint!

- The Holy Family (Joseph, Mary, and Jesus)
- St. Louis Martin and St. Zelie Guerin and their children, Marie, Pauline, Léonie, Helene, Céline, and St. Thérèse
- St. Gregory and St. Nonna and their children, St. Gorgonia, St. Caesareus, and St. Gregory of Nazianzus
- St. Gordianus and St. Silva, parents of St. Gregory the Great
- St. Monica and her son, St. Augustine
- St. Benedict and St. Scholastica (brother and sister)
- St. Clare and St. Agnes (sisters)

Why are they known for their holiness?

....

....

....

What were their struggles?

....

....

....

....

How can we learn from their lives to do better in our own?

....

....

....

....

....

Prayer Is the Cornerstone

Compose your own family prayer! It might help to use this outline:

- Invocation (address God or one of the persons of the Trinity)
- Gratitude (offer thanksgiving for the gift of your family)
- Petition for the needs of your family, or for God to bless your family
- Leave a "blank spot" for adding special intentions
- Close by invoking the name of your family's patron saint
- Amen!

Once you have composed your prayer, copy it onto the "prayer card" on the following page.

OUR FAMILY PRAYER

_____

_____

_____

_____

_____

_____

_____

_____

_____

_____

_____

Living Together Means Working Together

Chores and work may not be the most fun part of living together in a community, but that also makes them an important focus of intentional family living. If you do everything else right and skip the chore and work routines, you will still have a great amount of tension in your community. In order to be successful with any cleaning or work routines, you have to spend time in training and formation: both for you and for your kids.

In developing good chore habits and routines, you will actually be working toward the development of your own family rule, regardless of whether you choose to formalize it or not. Here are some tips to help that go better!

Some Tips for Sharing Household Work as a Family

1. Be stubborn.

First of all, be stubborn in your pursuit of a shared family work ethic. Not mean, obstinate, difficult, or disagreeable. Just stubborn. Refuse to give up until what you want to happen is happening.

2. Know your expectations.

You have to know what you want to have happen, because if you don't know what you want to have happen, your children definitely don't know!

3. Be realistic.

Of course, in knowing your expectations you bring yourself right along to the next point—the need to be realistic.

There are many things to be realistic about. Be realistic about how much independent work your children are capable of. Working together, everyone gets more done. Think of it as everyone eating a piece of the same pie and then moving on to the next pie instead of all eating one piece from your own pie and then having a bunch of partially eaten pies. Maybe pie is a bad example, but a bunch of partially finished jobs will add to you feeling that cleaning is a never-ending job.

Be realistic about quality. Have high expectations of quality, and don't be afraid to send someone back if they don't do a complete job, but make sure that your quality expectations are age appropriate. You should not expect the same quality window washing from a three-year-old and a thirteen-year-old.

4. Develop habits.

Habits are the key to the next tip: Be disciplined in developing habits for yourself and for your children. It is a habit to put shoes and coats in the proper place when you arrive at home. It is a habit to wipe down your kitchen counters when you finish preparing food. It is a habit to bend over and pick up a Kleenex that misses the garbage can. It is a habit to wipe out the sink if you make a mess of toothpaste. Once these sorts of small acts become habits we don't need checklists or long lists of cleaning tasks.

When developing habits, however, focus on one thing at a time. We didn't learn to read by trying to learn the entire alphabet and all the phonics rules in one sitting. We took it one letter at a time and small words built into bigger words with more complicated rules and systems. The same thing can go for learning to complete household work consistently and with quality.

5. Learn to laugh.

You will make mistakes, and so will your kids. Learn to laugh it off and fix it. I am chronically horrible about serving really messy lunches right after I mopped the floor. In seeing me joke about my mistake, kids are much more likely to have a lighthearted attitude towards their own work. The problem in our house is not making a mistake, it's not being willing to fix it. At the same time, allow yourself and your children to phone it in from time to time. Hard work is important, but sometimes we all need a little break.

6. Train children in the art of noticing.

Point out how enjoyable it is to pull up into the driveway and see the bikes all parked neatly. Sometimes, we will play a version of I-spy where I stand in the middle of the room and point out things I can see that are out of place while the children race to fix them. When they are older and working independently, I ask them to play I-spy on their own and see if they can stump me so I can't find anything when I check their job. Usually they will find a couple more things they missed when they were trying to rush through to finish (because they are kids, they still rush). The noticing game becomes a tool that helps older children work more independently.

7. Strike a balance.

Finally, strike a balance between work and play. I'm also all about having fun while you work so that it feels like play. Teaching children to have a joyful and helpful attitude about chores is all about helping them see why it matters. It matters because when our jobs are finished we have more time for fun, both as a family and as individuals. It matters because when our house is well cared for, we are better able to use our home as a tool to bless other people. It matters because it is more restful to relax in an orderly space. If housework is a stress point for you it will become a stress point for your children and a stress point between you (if it isn't already). It might not be the most enjoyable activity in this book, but it is still worth spending time on.

> ## A Bonus Mission
>
> With younger children, you may enjoy sharing a story to encourage a family work ethic. *One Morning In Maine*, by Robert McCloskey, is a picture story with many examples of how a family can work together while also enjoying their time throughout the day. It contains a positive reminder of the small ways that even young children can be helpful and the ways the adult attitude can reflect on a child's interruption.

DOING FAMILY MEETINGS: HOW WILL WE MAKE DECISIONS?

Working side by side, praying together, and playing together builds teamwork and relationships, but families also benefit from a time set aside for regular communication. The traditional family dinner hour is slipping away from many families as their calendars are crowded with more and more activities. Homework creeps into evening time that might be spent talking together, playing a game, or reading. The truth is, it isn't culturally cool to admit that you have too much on your family plate. Family meetings can provide a forum for building relationships, communicating about activities and schedule changes, and even just catching up between soccer practice and piano lessons.

My husband and I are both former classroom teachers, so our family meeting style is similar to what you might see in a school. We assign jobs for each meeting and everyone has a role to play. We take turns with jobs such as opening and closing prayer, humorist, moderator, note taker, and more. Kids and adults share equally in performing each of the roles. All of our family meetings have the same structure. We also keep our meeting materials in a family binder. The job signup is in the front plastic page protector and we write jobs with a dry erase marker and change them each week.

Family meetings are a time when we pray together, laugh together, and problem solve. We only have one bathroom for nine people, so problem solving a shower schedule is a family meeting problem. Yes, I could (and sometimes do) just provide a schedule/chart as a solution, but I've noticed that my kids respond a lot better to a solution when they help create it. Maybe one person is getting stuck walking the dog every time or two people are having a particularly difficult time in their relationship. Having a forum to discuss these issues when they arise contributes to an overall sense of peace in the family.

You may even want to keep a list in a designated place for kids to add to the agenda between meetings. Then during the meeting read through each item and see if it still needs to be addressed. You may find that many things make the list initially, but aren't still issues by the time you read the agenda. However, you have totally validated your child's voice by including it anyway and you can use the opportunity to compliment their handling of the issue in another way. With practice, kids will get better at knowing what is a family meeting issue and what is not.

Family meetings are a useful tool in the family problem-solving tool kit. With my own kids, we have vacillated between weekly and monthly meetings. There are advantages and disadvantages to each approach. Family meetings can be long or short and can happen at whatever interval works well for your family.

DISCUSSION

1. How does your family do most of its communicating right now? Looking at your schedule and existing routines, are there any family members who are being excluded from conversation? If so, why? Are there activities (kid or adult) that could be dropped or switched to another time so that you have more time as a family?

....

....

....

....

....

....

....

....

....

....

2. If you could open a conversation about any topic in your family, what would you talk about? Are there any specific challenges you want to tackle or things you want to study together?

....

....

....

....

....

....

....

....

....

....

....

....

ACTIVITIES FOR DOING FAMILY MEETINGS

Family Meetings Keep Us Organized

Create a family meeting binder to keep all of the papers you will use in the same place. Our family meeting binder has our family mission statement (Mission 3) printed on the front, along with various holy cards, prayers, and family photos to finish the front and back of the cover. Inside we have the printed part of any family bible studies, catechesis, or virtue training we are working with at that time. We also have a list of favorite family meals, our family rules to have more fun, meeting schedule, job assignments, and a few activity suggestions for rainy days.

A family meeting binder is a living document that changes to meet the needs of your family in a given time and place. And because it's portable, you can even hold family meetings on the road!

Family Meetings Need A Plan

While family meetings do not need to follow a set formula, it is good to have a consistent routine from week to week. Having a consistent routine helps kids feel more comfortable because they know what to expect.

While your family meeting agenda will vary depending on your changing circumstances, here are some jobs and agenda items to consider.

Jobs: humorist; moderator; prayer leader; secretary; time keeper. Feel free to give your jobs a fun name to fit your family personality: maybe giving each job or agenda item its own saint or using alliteration to make all the jobs start with the same letter.

Agenda items: opening/closing prayer; VIP check-in (highs and lows); schedule or calendar updates; discussion topics; awards; affirmations.

What roles and agenda items will your family meeting feature?

Roles	Agenda items

Family Meetings Have to Start Somewhere

There is really only one way to learn how to run effective family meetings. You've got to practice! Jump in and hold your first family meeting using the family meeting binder and agenda you've already created. Hint: Be sure to gather feedback about the meeting after your first one.

Reader of the Mission Statement

If your family has developed a mission statement, consider reading it at each family meeting.

Goal Check Up

Take a minute to check in with your goals. How is everyone doing? Anything we should work on a little more this week?

Prayer

You could choose to open and close your meeting with specific prayers or spontaneous prayers offered by an individual.

Discussion Time

Ideas for discussion topics include upcoming events, urgent family business (agenda created in advance), virtue training, family catechesis, study of Scripture, and more.

Humorist

Designate one person each week to tell a joke. You can have a joke book available. Check one out from the library or encourage children to create their own.

Scripture Reading

Read an entire Gospel aloud during a specific season (such as Lent), or do weekly Scripture study with the Sunday readings, or focus on a book of the Bible from start to finish.

Highs & Lows

This is a time for each person to share a high and a low from their week. They can share whatever they want and no one is allowed to argue with them. All opinions are valid!

MISSION 6

BEING HOLY: HOW DO WE KEEP THE FAITH IN A SECULAR WORLD?

The family is experiencing a profound cultural crisis, as are all communities and social bonds....

—Evangelii Gaudium #66

The family is the original cell of social life. It is the natural society in which husband and wife are called to give themselves in love and in the gift of life.... The family is the community in which, from childhood, one can learn moral values, begin to honor God, and make good use of freedom. Family life is an initiation into life in society.

—Catechism of the catholic Church #2207

In our modern day we are faced with increasingly difficult choices regarding the raising of Catholic children: Which schools? How much screen time? How about friends? What about social and sports activities?

As daunting as all these questions are, the Church affirms that we're up to the task—just because we're parents. "Parents are the first and most important educators of their own children," St. Pope John Paul II wrote in his 1994 *Letter to Families*, "and they also possess a fundamental competence in this area; they are educators, because they are parents" (#16 §7). Choosing the settings and resources for our children that will support our family's goals and beliefs, however, is not such an easy task.

We live in a crazy world, filled with ever-bolder examples of anti-Christian sentiment and media.

Part of parenting in an intentionally Catholic way is having a plan for navigating this world with our kids. When my first child was young it was easy to monitor everything he read and watched on TV. If I didn't like the content, I turned it off. It was rare that he would read a book before I read it first. I would carefully skip any "not nice" words when we read aloud with my son none the wiser.

This worked great for my children when they were young, but what about as kids grow? How do we teach children to discern the moral worth of a book? What should they do when they come across questionable or outright offensive content?

Over time, I've realized that while it is tempting to simply close the door on all books, music, other media, and even sometimes groups of people who reflect a non-Catholic perspective, it may not be the best way to go. Of course, prudence is required here and the age of the child, the type of content, and the mode of delivery all must be considered.

As parents, we have access to so much information! Potty training issues? Google it—someone has the answer! But simply transferring that person's solution to our own families doesn't always work out so great. The successful families I have observed in my years in the classroom are absolute bulldogs about researching the best approach to raising kids, but they are empowered to take that information and use it in a way that works for their family. Our culture would like to rob us of the ability to be the moral decision makers for our families, but we don't have to let it!

DISCUSSION

1. What is the most challenging area for you when it comes to raising your kids? School? Activities? Media usage? Movies and television? How do your kids feel about these issues?

....

....

....

....

....

....
....
....
....
....
....
....

2. What are some of your favorite sources for information on parenting and family topics? How are you adapting their knowledge to your family situation?

....
....
....
....
....
....
....
....
....
....
....

ACTIVITIES FOR KEEPING THE FAITH

Learning to Evaluate Media Critically

If we expose our children to what is good, true, and beautiful, and foster in them an appreciation for it, the landscape in their imaginations develops in a way that makes it easier to recognize unpalatable or biased content.

With young children, it is absolutely appropriate to protect their tender hearts and minds from as much inappropriate content as we can. We cannot completely shield our older children from such content, however, any more than we can entirely avoid it ourselves. We can, however, train older children to evaluate the moral worth of the media they are consuming. Sometimes we may need to put up our own roadblocks, but as children grow older, we also need to teach them to recognize negative media messages on their own and respond appropriately.

Here are three questions to help families discern which media are right for them. Use these questions together with your children at first so that they get in the habit of asking them anytime they watch a video or pick up a book, even on their own. You'll find a ready-made bookmark with a shortened version of these questions at the end of this journal (page 49)—photocopy it and cut it out, then have your kids decorate it.

1. How does this video/book/song/game affect me?

In many ways, this is the most important question, and you can start using it from a young age. Does watching Ninjago turn your five-year-old into a spinning, side-kicking crazy person who attacks everyone who walks by? Maybe they shouldn't watch that show any longer. But instead of just taking it away, make a connection between watching the show and the change in attitude you observed. Try saying something like this:

- "I don't see you being your best self."
- "I know you can make better decisions."
- "I want to help you behave your best."

For a young child, that is enough discussion on the matter. It's just enough to teach them to start thinking about what goes into their mind and what comes back out in their actions and attitudes.

My oldest son loves fantasy, which can be a dark genre. His moral compass is solid, and he had always handled reading them with no ill effects. One time, though, he was listening to an audio book series that seemed to put him in a dreary mood. After several days, I had a conversation with him emphasizing that I suspected his mind was spending a lot of time thinking about the dark parts of the story.

Being a young teen, he at first denied there was any correlation, but he humored me by switching to something lighter and more playful. His calm, cheerful disposition returned, and eventually he admitted that the darker book series had been affecting his behavior—something he could now see once he had been made aware of it.

This was the beginning of a great, ongoing conversation about how we feed ourselves spiritually and mentally, not just physically. We have also talked about how even something just "playing in the background" while he builds LEGOs or cleans his room can still affect him. The same principle can apply to video games, particularly those with fantasy-based violent content.

2. What is the purpose of continuing to consume this content?

When media choices are causing sinful or inappropriate behavior, stepping away from the media is the correct response. It may also be the correct response if the media causes scandal by introducing a child to something that is clearly beyond their ability to process.

Sometimes, however, there is a good reason for older children and adults to continue with the media content, even though that content is upsetting. Dark or disturbing elements of the content may ultimately serve a more noble purpose. The movie *Schindler's List*, for example, portrays violence and great human suffering, but those elements of the movie serve the larger purpose of increasing our compassion for others as well as our understanding of the Holocaust.

Younger children are not developmentally equipped to answer this question on their own, but tweens and teens should be able to make these judgments, with Mom and Dad only intervening when they see evidence of negative effects.

3. How did this content challenge or change me?

If a decision is made to continue with challenging content, it's important to come back to a safe place for conversation around this question. For tweens and teens this safe place should be their family and faith community. Not everything needs to be rehashed, disected, and discussed, but kids need to be given space to talk about content that raises moral, emotional, or faith questions for them.

Kids also need to be taught how to voice their own response to the media they consume. Maybe they decide to no longer read a particular author. Maybe they want to leave an online review making other parents and young readers aware of potential problems in a game, song or movie.

Maybe they feel called to action as a result of the great suffering they read about. Whatever their response may be, asking this question helps older kids process and respond to their experience in a way that benefits their overall growth and development.

Social Media Is Still A Choice

It might sound crazy, but you really don't "have" to be on social media if you would prefer not to be—and neither does your teen. Even in the twenty-first century, that is a valid choice.

Ultimately, you must make your own decision about whether your teen is ready for social media. In order to thrive in the world of social media, teens must have a well-grounded sense of their own dignity and the dignity of others. Sharing happens with the click of a button, but the consequences of a hasty choice can be life altering…or, in some cases, life-ending. If you and your child aren't ready to face that just yet, it might be better to wait before grabbing that new account.

Once your teen has jumped into the social media world, however, here are some specific questions that can help him or her make good social media decisions:

- Am I honoring God?
- Am I respecting the dignity of myself and others?
- Does my online behavior reflect that I am created for and by God?
- Am I supporting my family's mission?

Sit down and have an intentional discussion about social media use now. How might your family mission statement translate into values and boundaries online?

CLOSING THOUGHTS

What then shall we say to this? If God is for us, who can be against us?
—ROMANS 8:31

The tools I've shared here have definitely helped my family maintain strong relationships rooted in the values of our Catholic faith. At times, though, we've had to adapt these tools of intentional living to fit our new circumstances.

I am thinking in particular of a time when our family was managing a high-risk pregnancy along with a probably terminal diagnosis for our unborn daughter. While I was on bed rest, I spent most of my time finding places for my children to be during the day because I couldn't care for them. Financially, we needed my husband's insurance and paycheck, which meant he couldn't take off much time to offer help. Our typical routines were no longer possible. Indeed, we were completely at the mercy of other people's kindness for most of our basic needs.

But even as we departed from our typical routine, I realized just how valuable our previous investment in intentional family living had been. Although many things were falling apart, our relationships were not. The phrase from our mission statement, "We work together," was lived more fully than ever. Intentional family living was carrying us even when it seemed like we were ignoring it.

After our daughter Siena passed, we were able to use the structure of intentional family living as a support system for our family when nothing else made sense. Slowly, everything else came back around us. We were on the same page because, before this season of chaos, we made it a priority to be on the same page. It didn't happen overnight, and at many times, particularly when my children were all younger, I wondered why on earth we were trying. Yet over time, there it was.

Exactly where we needed it to be, right when we needed it to be there.

In closing, let me offer this encouragemnt: By living out your Catholic faith through intentional family living, you are giving a gift to yourself, your children, and your Church. Many things may be stacked against us in the current social climate, but Christ is always at our side. Reach out to God through prayer and the sacraments and he will help you make it happen.

Heidi

PRAYER TO THE HOLY FAMILY
BY POPE LEO XIII

Most Loving Jesus,
by your sublime and beautiful virtues
and by the example of Your family life
you blessed with peace and happiness
the family chosen by you on earth.
Graciously look on this family
humbly kneeling before You
and importing Your mercy.
Remember that we belong entirely to You,
for it is to You we have in a special way
dedicated and devoted ourselves.
Look on us in Your loving kindness,
preserve us from dangers,
and give us the grace to persevere
to the end in the imitation of Your Holy Family.
After revering and loving You faithfully on earth,
may we bless and praise You eternally in heaven.
Mary, our dearest Mother,
to your intercession we have recourse,
knowing that your diving Son will hear your prayers.
Glorious patriarch, St. Joseph,
assist us by your powerful mediation,
and offer by the hands of Mary our prayers to Jesus.
Jesus, Mary, and Joseph, enlighten us, assist us, save us.

Amen.

8 TRAITS OF PRUDENT PARENTS

1. Know Yourself

Being a prudent parent starts with knowing yourself, including your strengths and weaknesses. Once you know your abilities, you are better able to take care of yourself and then better able to take care of your family.

2. Know the Members of Your Family

Once you know your own strengths and weaknesses, it's time to get to know the other members of your family—in the way that is only possible through an authentic, intimate relationship with one another. Whether you have one child or twelve, they are all individuals with their own strengths and weaknesses that contribute to the family dynamic.

3. Be an Avid Researcher

Once you know yourself and the members of your family in a deep, meaningful way, seek outside expertise to address your particular parenting situation.

4. Adapt Expert Advice to Your Situation

Prudent parents don't just implement new research or expert opinions; rather, they adapt it to suit their own strengths and weaknesses and those of their family members.

5. Surround Yourself with Successful Families

Confident families tend to come in groups. They spend time with other families with similar values and expectations. These groups tend to cross generational boundaries, with older couples informally mentoring younger ones. Many people travel great distances to attend a parish or school that is supportive of their family's gifts and charisms.

6. Have Clear Expectations, Goals, and a Mission Statement

This journal has included a fair amount of information on goals and mission statements already. The only thing I want to add is that knowing expectations is contagious. If you don't know your own expectations, neither will your children.

7. Don't Be Afraid to Make Mistakes

Prudent parents aren't afraid of their mistakes. They know they will make them and even laugh at them. Laughing at mistakes even helps build knowledge of one another!

8. Don't Be Afraid to March to Your Own Family Beat

Confident families know what they want. They surround themselves with resources to support them on their journey. They build relationships. The most important trait I've noticed, however, is that prudent families do not apologize for marching to their own beat. They know that there are many valid ways to raise a family and believe they have chosen the best one for their family.

ABOUT THE AUTHOR

Heidi Indahl, M. Ed., is a Catholic speaker, author, blogger, and most importantly, wife and mother. A former classroom teacher who now homeschools her children, she began blogging as a way to keep in touch with other moms as they stumbled their way through the early years of parenthood. Her blogging grew into a ministry of family living and homeschool support. Her first book, *Blessed Is the Fruit of Thy Womb: Rosary Reflections for Miscarriage, Stillbirth, & Infant Loss* was originally published in 2017. She is also the author of *67 Ways to Do the Works of Mercy With Your Kids*. Both titles are available from Our Sunday Visitor.

This project was first conceived during work on her masters of education in instructional design as a way to encourage parents in their role as teachers and leaders in their own families.

Heidi and her family spend their time building fences, planting gardens, and caring for critters on their eight-acre fixer-upper homestead. As a break, she enjoys a good book with an even better cup of tea. Her favorite social media is definitely Instagram, and she would love to "see" you over there (@workandplaydaybyday).

1. How is this affecting me?
2. Why am I using it?
3. How did it change or challenge me?

1. How is this affecting me?
2. Why am I using it?
3. How did it change or challenge me?

1. How is this affecting me?
2. Why am I using it?
3. How did it change or challenge me?

Printed in Great Britain
by Amazon